Cat Brac

Danny Pearson

Illustrated by Seb Camagajevac

GEMS

Titles in GEMS

Badger Publishing Limited
Oldmedow Road,
Hardwick Industrial Estate,
King's Lynn PE30 4JJ
Telephone: 01438 791037
www.badgerlearning.co.uk

Cat Brace Face ISBN 978-1-78147-477-8

Text © Danny Pearson 2013
Complete work © Badger Publishing Limited 2013

Publisher: Susan Ross
Senior Editor: Danny Pearson
Design: Julia King
Illustrator: Seb Camagajevac

2 4 6 8 10 9 7 5 3 1

Cat Brace Face

Contents

Vocabulary:

almighty	pounced
slammed	speechless
surrounded	swarm

Main characters:

Kim

Ginger

Chapter 1
Trip to the dentist

Kim had been dreading this trip to the dentist.

She was being fitted with braces for her teeth. She knew they would help, but she was worried about what people at school would say.

"There we are, all done," said the dentist. "Would you like to take a look?"

Kim nodded sadly with her eyes closed.

The dentist raised a mirror to show Kim her face. She slowly opened her eyes and smiled.

"Wow!" she shrieked. You could hardly see them.

"See, nothing to worry about at all," said the dentist with a smile.

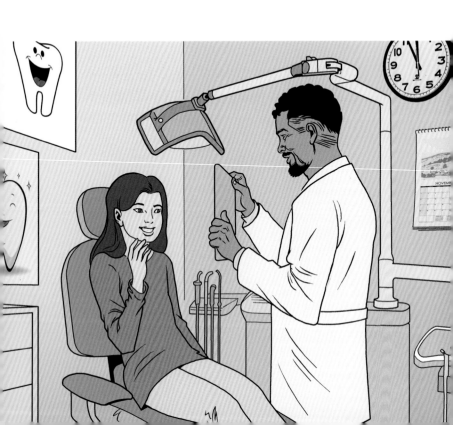

The next day Kim rode into school on her bike. She met her friend Hannah at the school gates.

"Let's have a look, then," said Hannah.

Kim smiled at her.

"Nice," beamed Hannah. "You can hardly see them."

"Hah, metal mouth!" shouted a voice from across the playground.

It was Olivia with her friends. She was the biggest girl in their year and she never had anything nice to say.

Olivia walked over to them. "That's a lot of metal you have in your mouth, Kim. I could see it from the other side of the playground."

"Leave her alone, Olivia, you can hardly see them," Hannah said.

"Shut it, you!" snapped Olivia.

Kim felt ugly and stared at the floor. "It's OK, Hannah, let's go."

She locked up her bike and made her way to class with Hannah. Olivia and her friends were laughing at her.

"See you later, brace face!" shouted Olivia from across the playground, for everyone to hear.

Chapter 2

Voice in the park

It had been a long day for Kim and she couldn't wait to get home. On her way through the local park she suddenly heard a voice.

"Help, please somebody, help!"

Kim got off her bike and looked around to see where it was coming from. She couldn't see anybody.

"HELP!" she heard again from above.

She looked, but all she could see was a small, ginger cat high up in the tree.

"Hello?" Kim called back.

"Please help me. I climbed up this tree and now I can't get down," the cat seemed to say.

Kim could not believe her eyes and ears but she called up again to the cat. "Hi, my name is Kim. I can help. I'll hold out my jacket and you can jump into it. I'll catch you!"

The cat now looked equally as shocked as Kim, but it had no choice. "OK!" the cat shouted back.

Kim held out her jacket. "On the count of three, you jump and I'll catch you!"

The cat got ready to jump.

"One... two... three!" shouted Kim.

The cat leapt and fell right into Kim's jacket. It sprang out as quickly as it had fallen, onto the grass.

It shook its little head and looked up at Kim.

"Are you OK?" asked Kim.

"Yes, perfectly fine, thank you." And with that, it shot off through the park.

Kim stood there, speechless. "Did that just happen?" she asked herself.

She got back on her bike and continued her journey home.

Chapter 3
Cat conversation

It was late and Kim was asleep in her bed. It was a hot, summer night and her bedroom window was open, letting in a gentle breeze.

She was woken by a conversation coming from outside her window.

"That's her, that's the one," she heard them say.

She slowly got up out of bed and made her way to the window. She was very tired and was in no mood to be woken up so late.

"Shh, she's coming," whispered one of the voices.

She looked out into the garden and could not see anybody, but she felt as if someone was watching her. She looked across to a nearby branch where she could see two cats sitting, staring at her.

Kim did not want to appear crazy, but she leaned out of the window and started to speak. "Excuse me, I don't know if you can understand me, but just in case you can, could you please be quiet and go away. I have school tomorrow and I really need to get some sleep."

The two cats opened their eyes wide and looked at one another in shock.

With two loud meows they raced down the tree trunk and sprang over the fence into the neighbour's garden.

Kim shut the window and shook her head. She wondered if it was the cats she had heard talking to one another.

Had she been able to speak to the cat earlier in the park? Did her new braces have anything to do with it?

She had too many questions racing around her head and she was far too sleepy to think about it all now.

She flopped back into bed and fell asleep.

Chapter 4
Cat Alley

BEEP! BEEP! BEEP! went Kim's alarm.

She reached over to switch it off, feeling more tired than she had been before she had gone to bed. It was time to get ready for school.

"Good morning, princess," said her dad, who was sitting at the breakfast table.

"Did you sleep well?" he asked.

"Yes, fine, thanks," she replied. There was no way she was going to tell him about her cat problem.

She ate her breakfast and headed off on her bike to school.

On her way down the street, Kim felt as if someone was watching her again and she looked to her side. There, to her right, was a cat running alongside her. She looked to her left. A cat was running alongside her there, too.

Everywhere around her, more cats were appearing over walls and fences.

There was soon a swarm of lots of different kinds of cats all around her. They seemed to steer her down an alley just off the road.

The alley was dark and she noticed a dead end up ahead.

She slammed on her brakes and looked behind her. She was trapped!

The cats started to close in on her.

She got off her bike.

"Get away from me!" Kim cried.

They were still slowly closing in on her, their eyes fixed on hers. She climbed on top of a bin to try and get over a wall. A huge, fat cat blocked her escape.

"Where do you think you're going?" it hissed.

The cat was like a giant, mean-looking fur ball.

It was twice the size of a normal cat and it had a fat face with a scar running down one side.

Kim leapt back down and backed up against the wall. She was surrounded. "What do you want from me?" she asked.

The fat cat leapt onto the bin lid. "So it's true, you can understand us... very interesting."

The others seemed to be talking amongst themselves. "Who is she? How can she hear us?" they were all whispering.

"Look, I don't know what you want from me. I have no idea how I can hear you, but it's OK, I'll keep it a secret if that's what you want," Kim pleaded.

The fat cat stared at her with an evil look on its face. "I'm sorry, my dear, but we simply can't have a human running around listening in on what we cats are up to. We need to put a stop to this now."

With that, all of the other cats started to close in on her. They were licking their lips and hissing at her.

Suddenly, the ginger cat from the park leapt over the wall and in front of Kim.

"Stop!" it screamed. "Stop at once. This human saved me yesterday."

"Move aside," the fat cat ordered.

The ginger cat stood its ground. "NO! Don't you see, she could help us?"

Kim spoke up. "That's right, I could help you. I could give you a warm place to stay, the finest fish, whatever you want, just don't hurt me."

All the cats paused and looked up at the fat cat.

"Interesting," he said. "Very interesting. OK, we may have a use for you, after all." He licked his paw and wiped his face. "A warm place to stay, you say?"

Kim nodded quickly. "Yes."

He licked his paw and wiped his face again. "The FINEST fish, you say?"

Kim nodded again. "Yes."

The fat cat sat on his back legs and looked at the crowd of cats. "Very well, the girl is with us now."

All of the cats meowed loudly and the ginger cat leapt into Kim's arms and started to purr.

Chapter 5

Running free

After school Kim went to the supermarket and bought the biggest fish she could find and headed back to her home. She had arranged for the cats to meet her at her house and she needed to get back before her parents returned from work.

She went round the back of her house, where she was greeted by the fat cat, with about twenty other cats.

She pulled out the fish from her school bag. "I have a treat for you."

"Yum, yum!" went the cats and they pounced on it.

Kim looked on with a raised eyebrow. "OK, now that's dinner dealt with. Let me show you to your new home."

She led them down to the bottom of the garden, to the shed. "Now, I know it isn't much at the moment but we can work on it."

The fat cat entered the big shed. "Mmm, yes, this will do. We can have a basket over in that corner and a few pillows over there. Yes, this will do nicely."

Kim thought that now was her chance. "Now I'd like to ask a favour of you."

The fat cat looked up at her, along with his friends. "Don't push your luck, little girl. You're lucky we chose to spare you."

Kim started to sweat. "I know, but it's just a small favour. I'll fetch you another great big fish tomorrow if you help me."

The fat cat's eyes lit up. "What is it you want?" he asked.

Kim bent down and whispered something into his ear.

He started to laugh. "Very nice, yes, we can certainly help you there."

The next day Kim rode up to the school gates to meet her friend Hannah.

"Metal mouth!" shouted Olivia from across the playground.

Hannah looked at Kim. "Just ignore her, Kim, she's just being a bully."

"It's OK, I've got this," Kim said with a smile.

She stood up tall and gave out an almighty MEOOOOOW!

From nowhere, cats of all shapes and sizes crashed through the school gates and over the playground walls. They headed straight for Olivia, who wasn't laughing now.

They chased her around the playground and into the school.

Everyone stood there with their mouths open in shock. Everyone but Kim, who stood with a smile on her face and her little ginger cat perched on her shoulder.

Questions

Why did Kim go to the dentist?

Was she pleased with the dentist's work?

How would you describe Hannah and Olivia?

What happened in the park on Kim's way home from school? Why was it unusual?

What woke Kim up that night? What did she do about it?

Do you think Kim's braces had anything to do with her hearing cats talk?

Can you describe the fat cat in the alley? What did he look like? How did he behave?

What did Kim offer the cats to stop them being angry with her?

Were the cats happy with Kim's gifts?

What did Kim ask for in return?